Six Silly P

Paul Groves

Star Plays
Series Editor: *Roy Blatchford*

Longman

Contents

1 Crazy Court

A court should be a place of order, dignity and justice. But it is not quite like that in the court of Mr Justice Thick. In fact it is plain crazy.

Characters	Usher
	Clerk
	Judge – Mr Justice Thick
	Foreman of the jury
	Jurywoman 1
	Counsel
	Mrs Scroggins
	Policeman 1
	Policewoman 1
	Cleaner (female)
	Ivor Shiftyface
	Jurywoman 2
	Jurywoman 3
	Mrs Shiftyface
	Rose E Parker

1 *A courtroom filled with people*

The usher enters

Usher Pray rise for the judge.

Clerk That's not fair.

Usher What's not fair?

Clerk Why should he have a pay rise? I haven't had one.

Usher I said 'pray rise' not pay rise, you fool. Pray rise for Mr Justice Thick.

The court rises as the judge enters

Judge Right, let's get on with it. What case are we to hear today?

Clerk	You can't hear a case, mi lud. Cases don't talk.
Judge	I mean law case, you fool. Not a suitcase. Come on. They open in half an hour.

The clerk hands the judge a paper

Clerk	The charge, mi lud.
Judge	Charge? I don't have to pay to come here, do I?
Clerk	No. I mean the criminal's offence.
Judge	He's not made of wood, is he?
Clerk	Wood, mi lud?
Judge	You said he's a fence. Ha! Ha! Got my own back.

Laughter in court

Clerk	Oh dear. I'm just as thick as what you are. Get it. Justice Thick.
Judge	Enough of this tomfoolery. Let's get on. They open in twenty-eight minutes.

There is chatter in the courtroom

Usher	Ush! Ush! Ush!
Judge	Why are you saying 'ush'?
Usher	I'm the usher.
Judge	That's a good enough reason. Let's get the jury in and make a start. They open in twenty-seven minutes.

A man stands up

Who are you?

Foreman	I'm the foreman, mi lud.
Judge	But you're only one man.
Foreman	No. I'm the foreman, mi lud.
Judge	Are you telling me I need glasses. I can see you and you're *one* man.
Clerk	He means the foreman of the jury.
Judge	But there are eleven men in a jury, not four.

Clerk	Twelve, mi lud.
Judge	Don't be so pernickety. What's one here or there? They open in twenty-six minutes. Swear in the jury.
Clerk	Do you swear . . .?
Jury-woman 1	I never swear, the idea . . .
Judge	He doesn't mean bloody.
Jury-woman 1	Really, mi lud. From your lips
Judge	He means take the oath.
Jury-woman 1	But I've never taken anything in my life. *(crying)* I'm a law abiding woman.
Judge	All right. All right. Forget it.
Counsel	I object to one of the jury, mi lud.
Judge	Which one do you object to?
Counsel	Mrs Scroggins.
Judge	Why do you object to Mrs Scroggins?
Counsel	She's my wife.
Judge	Stand up, Mrs Scroggins.

A woman stands up

Good God! I would object to her myself.

Mrs Scroggins	Just wait till I get you home.
Judge	Now I want no threats in my court. Indeed I want no threats. Shut up or I'll give you a knuckle sandwich. Sit down, jury.
Foreman	We can't sit down, mi lud, there aren't any seats.
Judge	What's happened to the benches?
Clerk	They've been pinched, mi lud.
Judge	Pinched! The benches pinched from a court of law. What are the police doing?

Clerk	Building a November the fifth bonfire, mi lud.
Judge	Oh well. Put in some deckchairs.
Clerk	Right, mi lud.
Usher	Call twelve deckchairs!
Clerk	Call twelve deckchairs!
Policeman 1	Call twelve deckchairs!
Police-woman 1	Call twelve deckchairs!

Noise of deckchairs being brought

Foreman	How do you put them up, mi lud?
Judge	You put the long end on the floor, lift it and put in the short end.
Clerk	No, mi lud, you put the short end on the floor, lift it and put in the long end.
Usher	What do you do with the medium end?
Judge	Oh, forget it. They can sit on the floor. Call the accused.
Usher	Call Ivor Shiftyface!
Clerk	Call Ivor Shiftyface!
Policeman 1	Call Ivor Shiftyface!
Police-woman 1	Call Ivor Shiftyface!

A woman enters

Judge	What are you doing in a dress, Mr Shiftyface?
Cleaner	I'm not Ivor Shiftyface.
Judge	Who are you then?
Cleaner	I'm the court cleaner. Mind out.

Sound of bucket

Judge	You can't clean the court now.
Cleaner	Why not?
Judge	We're in session.

Cleaner	You're in a lot of muck, too.
Judge	Oh well, you'd better do it now. I need to brush up on my law for this case. Get it, Clerk? Brush up on my law.

Laughter breaks out again in the courtroom

Usher	Order! Order!
Judge	I'll have bangers and beans.
Usher	I mean 'ush', mi lud. Ush! Ush!
Judge	Well, let's hurry up, they open in twenty minutes. Call the accused!
Usher	Call Ivor Shiftyface!
Clerk	Call Ivor Shiftyface!
Judge	Do we have to go through all this again?
Usher	Yes, mi lud.
Judge	Oh very well.
Policeman 1	Call Ivor Shiftyface!
Police- woman 1	Call Ivor Shiftyface!
Clerk	Are you Ivor Shiftyface?
Ivor	Yes, mate.
Judge	Why didn't you come when you were called?
Ivor	I forgot my name, mate.
Judge	How can you forget a name like . . . er . . . er . . . What's he called?
Clerk	Shiftyface, mi lud.
Judge	Like Shiftyface?
Ivor	I have lapses of memory, mate.
Judge	Don't call me mate!
Ivor	Sorry, cock.
Judge	That's better.
Clerk	Stand in the dock.

Ivor	I'm not a ship.
Judge	It's not that kind of dock, cock . . . I mean mate. What do I mean? Read out the charge.
Clerk	Ivor Shiftyface you are charged that on the evening of the fourth of June you did steal from McBride's Fish Bar.
Judge	I didn't know fish drank beer.
Clerk	A fish and chip shop, mi lud.
Judge	Oh. Which reminds me, they open in fifteen minutes.
Clerk	You did steal two portions of chips value 50p and two pieces of plaice value 100p.
Judge	Any scraps?
Clerk	There was no fight, mi lud.
Judge	No, I mean those little bits of batter. I love them.
Jury-woman 2	So do I. Can we send out for some now?
	Cries of 'yes'
Usher	Ush! Ush!
Clerk	How do you plead?
Ivor	Quite badly, if I cut myself shaving.
Judge	Plead! Not bleed, you fool.
Clerk	Are you guilty or not guilty?
Ivor	Neither, I'm Shiftyface.
Judge	He meant: Did you nick the stuff?
Ivor	No, cock.
Policeman 1	Excuse me, mi lud, someone has left a Jaguar outside on the double yellow lines.
Judge	Wild animals outside my court? What next?
Policeman 1	No, a car, mi lud. Registration: NUT 120Y.
Judge	That's a serious offence. I fine them £50.

Clerk	It's your car, mi lud.
Judge	I mean 10p. Here take this, constable, and go and feed a meter.
Ivor	Give it two portions of chips and two of plaice.
Judge	That's enough of that.

Laughter in court

Usher	Order! Order!
Judge	Two double whiskies.
Usher	I mean 'ush', mi lud.
Judge	Well, why don't you say so. I keep getting all hungry and thirsty. Let's get on with it. Counsel for the Prosecution, can you begin?
Counsel	I have my briefs here, mi lud.
Judge	I should hope so. I want no one in my court without underpants.
Counsel	No, I have the papers here, mi lud.
Judge	Can I have the racing page, there's a . . .
Counsel	My law papers, mi lud.
Judge	Well, get on with it then.
Cleaner	Shift over a bit. I want to sweep round your feet.
Judge	Really.
Cleaner	Bringing all that wet in from the rain. I don't know.
Jury-woman 3	Did you say rain. I've left my washing out. I must get it in.

She exits

Clerk	Come back, madam. She's gone, mi lud.
Judge	Now we're one short in the jury. What can we do, clerk?
Ivor	If I may make a suggestion, cock. There's a dear old lady sitting outside who would love to be on a jury.

Judge	Capital. Call her in, constable.
Clerk	But, mi lud.
Judge	Call her in, constable.

An old lady enters

Hurry up they open in ten minutes. Ah, are you willing to serve on a jury?

Mrs Shifty-face	Serve what?
Ivor	Tennis balls.
Clerk	Be on a jury.
Mrs Shifty-face	I should love to.

She goes over to Ivor

Hello, duck. Give us a kiss then.

Ivor	Mother!
Mrs Shifty-face	Isn't he a lovely boy?
Judge	Yes, but haven't I seen that face somewhere else?
Ivor	No it's always been on the top of my neck.
Judge	I mean your mother. Never mind. Proceed, Counsel.
Counsel	I'll call my first witness.
Usher	Call Rose E Parker.
Clerk	Call Rose E Parker.
Policeman 1	Call Rose E Parker.
Police-woman 1	Call Rose E Parker.

A woman enters

Clerk	Are you Rose E Parker.
Rose	Yes.
Judge	Thank goodness for that. Hurry up with your evidence.

They open in six minutes.

Clerk	Take the stand, Mrs Parker.
Judge	I don't want her taking the stand. I mean someone's nicked the benches already.
Clerk	That just means stand there, mi lud. In the witness stand.
Judge	Oh!
Rose	Can't I sit down?
Judge	You can't sit in a stand.
Rose	You can at a football match.
Judge	But this is not a football match. This is a court of law. Let's have some dignity.

He takes out a cigar

Can I have a light, clerk?

Clerk	No, but you can have a heavy clerk, mi lud. Ha! Ha!

Laughter in court

Usher	Ush! Ush!
Judge	I shall fine you in a minute for making terrible jokes.
Rose	It's me corns, you see.
Judge	All right, get her a deckchair.
Clerk	Do you swear . . .?
Judge	We don't want all that. They open in four minutes.
Counsel	Rose Parker, where were you on the night of the fourth of June?
Rose	I was in bed.
Counsel	No, at eight o'clock.
Rose	I was in McBride's Fish Bar queuing up when a man came in front of me. He had a striped jumper and a stocking over his head.
Judge	What a dreadful crime, pushing into a fish and chip queue. That's a life sentence at least!

Counsel	Can you see that man in court?
Rose	Yes, it was him.

She points at the judge

Counsel	That's the Judge, you fool.
Rose	Let me put my glasses on. It was him.

Points at Ivor

Cleaner	I can prove that it was not my client, mi lud.
Judge	I thought you were the court cleaner, not a counsel.
Cleaner	Who better than me to make him come clean, mi lud.
Judge	You have a point there.
Cleaner	I can prove that he was not in McBride's Fish Bar on the night of the fourth of June.
Judge	How can you prove it?
Cleaner	Because he was pinching the Crown Jewels at the time. He could not be in two places at once.
Judge	Well, that seems to prove it. Jury, how do you find him?
Foreman	You don't have to find him, he's here already, mi lud.
Judge	I mean guilty or not guilty.
Foreman	We think you should let him off.
Ivor	I object.
Judge	Why do you object?
Ivor	I don't want to be let off. I'm not a firework.
Judge	Now I know where I have seen that face before. Isn't it Norah?
Mrs Shifty-face	Arnold!
Judge	My long lost love.
Mrs Shifty-face	Let's get married at once.

Judge	If your son comes on honeymoon with us.
Ivor	Certainly, if you help me with this case.
Judge	I have helped you.
Ivor	No, this suitcase. *(Winks)* It's got something . . . *(Winks)* rather precious in it. *(Winks)*
Judge	Constable, take it to the airport.
Usher	Mi lud, they're open.
Judge	What are we doing here then?

A stampede of Judge, jury, police and public.

2 Holiday Cottage

Do your family argue about where to go on holiday and how much to spend on it? The Tufton family do. Mr Tufton always likes a cheap holiday. And they can't come much cheaper than Seaview Cottage at the holiday resort of Mudhampton.

Characters	Mr Tufton
	Mrs Tufton
	Gran Tufton
	Wayne Tufton
	Melvyn Tufton
	Janice Tufton
	Helen Tufton
	A Countryman

1 *Remote countryside*

The Tuftons are in their car

Mrs Tufton	Is it much further?
Mr Tufton	It can't be. Wayne, are you looking at the map?
Wayne	Yes.
Mr Tufton	Well, how much further?
Wayne	We seem to be going backwards.
Mr Tufton	What do you mean backwards?
Wayne	We're getting further from Mudhampton not closer.
Melvyn	Let me look. You fool, you're looking at the road to *Muck*hampton not *Mud*hampton.
Mrs Tufton	Oh, Wayne.
Mr Tufton	Don't they teach you to read at school these days?
Gran	Are we there yet?

Mrs Tufton	No, Gran.
Gran	I could do with a cup of tea.
Melvyn	I could do with a plate of chips.
Helen	I feel sick.
Melvyn	Nice greasy ones.
Helen	You pig!
Mr Tufton	Don't you two start fighting.
Helen	Can't you stop?
Mr Tufton	Use your plastic bag.
Helen	You don't care about me.
Mrs Tufton	Look, there's a man. Stop and ask him.
Mr Tufton	All right.

He stops the car

Can you direct me to Seaview Cottage?

Countryman	Yum ar ter lef flee rook nur the tray.
Mr Tufton	I beg your pardon.
Countryman	Yum ar ter lef flee rook nur the tray.
Mr Tufton	Thank you.
Countryman	Ah noggins to ye.
Mr Tufton	Did you understand a word he said?
Mrs Tufton	No.
Mr Tufton	We'll have to rely on the map.

He starts the car

Mrs Tufton	Stop!
Mr Tufton	It's no good asking that old fool. He doesn't speak English.
Mrs Tufton	No Helen.
Mr Tufton	What about Helen?

Mrs Tufton	She's back there in the hedge.
Mr Tufton	I didn't know she had got out.

He slams on the brakes

Wayne	I think he said turn left by the tree with the three rooks in it.
Mr Tufton	How stupid.
Wayne	Why?
Mr Tufton	Well, rooks fly away, you fool. How does he know three rooks will be in a tree.
Melvyn	They're not daft these countrymen.
Helen	You were going off without me.

She starts to cry

Mrs Tufton	There, dear.
Helen	You don't care.
Mr Tufton	Get in it'll be dark soon.

They set off again

Janice	Look there's a signpost!
Mr Tufton	It's half broken.
Melvyn	It says 'Seav . . .'.
Wayne	That must be it.
Mr Tufton	Why?
Wayne	There's a tree with three rooks in it.
Mr Tufton	I don't believe it.

They turn down a narrow pot-holed lane

Mr Tufton	You and your tree full of rooks. This can't be it. We must have gone three miles.
Mrs Tufton	Keep going, dear.
Mr Tufton	Look at the pot-holes.
Janice	It can't be much farther.

Mr Tufton	My suspension.
Gran	What's the matter with his suspender belt?
Mrs Tufton	No, Gran, it's the car.
Helen	Can't you stop rocking the car up and down ... my stomach!
Mr Tufton	They're a foot deep.
Mrs Tufton	Well, you wanted to rent a holiday cottage in the country. I wanted to stay in a hotel. It's no holiday for me cooking for you lot.
Mr Tufton	It's too dear in a hotel. Besides this cottage is a bargain and think of all that fresh country food it said in the advert.
Melvyn	Yes, thick rich cream.
Helen	Shut up.
Mr Tufton	Damn!
Mrs Tufton	What is it?
Mr Tufton	We're stuck down a pot-hole.
Wayne	Reverse.
Mr Tufton	I'm trying – it's stuck fast.
Melvyn	It can't be stuck fast. It must be stuck slow.
Mr Tufton	No jokes at a time like this Melvyn or I'll belt you.
Mrs Tufton	Dad, such language! What a way to start a holiday.
Wayne	I'll get out and see what I can do.
Mr Tufton	I'm not having you messing about with my car again.
Wayne	Oh, Dad.
Gran	Can I get out and unpack?
Mrs Tufton	We're not there yet, Gran.
Janice	Look, there's a cottage there!
Melvyn	It's across two fields.
Wayne	That must be it. There's no other building.

Mr Tufton	What a place!
Mrs Tufton	You wanted to have some fresh air this holiday.
Melvyn	I don't know about fresh air but there's plenty of fresh manure. Look at all those cows.
Mrs Tufton	You know I can't stand cows.
Gran	I think the Isle of Wight's lovely.
Mr Tufton	What do you mean the Isle of Wight?
Gran	I think Cowes is a lovely place.
Mr Tufton	No, Gran, oh forget it. We'll have to make the best of it and carry the luggage there. Then we'll get a tractor to pull this car out. Come on you kids.
Melyn/ Janice	Oh, Dad.
Helen	I'm too sick to carry things.
Wayne	I've got an idea.
Mr Tufton	I don't want any of your ideas. Get carrying.

2 *Outside the holiday cottage*

Mrs Tufton	Just look at my tights.
Janice	Look at mine.
Mrs Tufton	Haven't they heard of paths and gates here? I blame you, Dad.
Mr Tufton	I didn't know we would have to climb through a hedge.
Gran	Wasn't it fun?
Janice	Just look at this garden. It's all weeds.
Mr Tufton	Damn.
Mrs Tufton	What is it?
Mr Tufton	I've left the key to the cottage in the car.
Wayne	It doesn't matter.
Mr Tufton	Why not?

Wayne	The door seems to have fallen off.
Mrs Tufton	I can't sleep in a place without a door. I blame you for this. Holiday cottage indeed! We should have gone to a hotel.
Mr Tufton	It's probably all right inside.
Melvyn	If it's got an inside.

3 Inside the cottage

Helen	Atishoo. I'm sickening for something.
Mrs Tufton	It's the dust.
Mr Tufton	You must expect a bit of dust in a country cottage.
Mrs Tufton	What five centimetres thick.
Wayne	It's not dust. No, it's flies.
Helen	Oh no. Where's the toilet?
Mr Tufton	Look here's a book. 'Welcome to Seaview Cottage'. Read it, Wayne. My glasses are in the car.
Wayne	To see the sea get ladder from barn and climb on to roof. Stand on tiptoe and you can see the sea.
Melvyn	Well, that's something.
Wayne	. . . if the tide is in.
Mrs Tufton	Give me a cup of tea before I faint.
Wayne	Tea . . . water. The well is one hundred metres over the field. Remove any dead sheep before drawing water.
Helen	I can't find the toilet.
Gran	It's nice and quiet here, isn't it?
Mrs Tufton	He booked the place. He can get any water we need.
Wayne	Wholemeal country bread.
Gran	Nice. Can I have mine now?
Wayne	The scythe is in the barn. Cut corn from the lower field.

	Thresh it in the barn. Grind between the two stones. Yeast is in the cupboard.
Melvyn	We don't have to cultivate that then.
Mrs Tufton	I don't believe this.
Wayne	Chop down old apple trees for fire to make bread.
Mr Tufton	Well, this holiday will certainly get the children fit.
Janice	What do you mean the children? What about you?
Helen	I've found the toilet but I can't use it.
Melvyn	Don't tell me. Get spade . . . dig trench in ground.
Helen	No, it's outside and there's a pig in it.
Melvyn	It must be a well-trained animal.
Wayne	Country butter. Milk cow. Put milk in churn. Churn for half an hour.
Janice	It would be easier to shake the cow up and down.
Wayne	Eggs. Round up chickens by making clucking sound.
Mrs Tufton	I must lie down before I faint.
Wayne	Beds . . .
Mrs Tufton	Thank goodness there are beds.
Wayne	. . . get straw from barn.
Mrs Tufton	Oh no.
Wayne	Spread ten centimetres deep on floor.
Mrs Tufton	Right I'm going to a hotel. Where's the phone?
Wayne	Phone. Light fire in field. Send up two puffs for a taxi, three for a . . .
Mrs Tufton	Right – Dad, get collecting some sticks.
Mr Tufton	Yes, I do think it would be best if we go.
Mrs Tufton	You're not going yet.
Mr Tufton	Not going?
Mrs Tufton	You're staying here to get that car out of that hole.

4 *In the lane*

An hour later

Mr Tufton   Just think they've left me here all alone. It's dark and starting to rain. I can't find my torch. Ah thank goodness, here comes somebody. Good evening. Can you tell me where I can find someone with a tractor?

Countryman Furt wurgle par for leen.

Mr Tufton   Oh, no!

3 It's a Fair Cop

The Dewars live in a quiet, respectable street in suburbia. But really they are burglars. One night Mr Dewar goes out to burgle and...

Characters	Mr Dewar
	Mrs Dewar
	Lightfingered Louie
	Joan-the-Snatch
	Gasman 1
	Gasman 2
	Policeman 1
	Policewoman 1
	Policeman 2
	Policewoman 2
	Policeman 3
	Policewoman 3

1 The Dewar's lounge

It is well furnished – in pride of place is a cabinet full of silver

Mrs Dewar   Must you go out tonight?

Mr Dewar   Yes, dear.

Mrs Dewar   That'll be the fourth night you've been out this week.

Mr Dewar   I know, dear.

Mrs Dewar   We've only been married six months and you keep leaving me like this.

Mr Dewar   It's my job, dear.

Mrs Dewar   I thought we might watch some telly and have an early night.

Mr Dewar   I'll try and be back early.

Mrs Dewar	It's not as if you've got much this week.
Mr Dewar	Tonight will be the big one. I feel it.
Mrs Dewar	I mean just that clock for three nights out.
Mr Dewar	I'm screwing a house in Surrey Road tonight. I've been casing it on these other nights. You don't realise the spadework that has to be put in. It'll be the big one.
Mrs Dewar	Promises. Promises.
Mr Dewar	Give us a kiss then.
Mrs Dewar	I'm going to bed. I'll give you a kiss when you get back with the loot. I think I'll take one of my pills.

She goes out. Mr Dewar picks up a large bag and leaves. There is a noise at the French windows followed by a faint sound of breaking glass. Lightfingered Louie and Joan-the-Snatch creep in

Louie	They've gone out. I saw the car go out. That trick of leaving the light on didn't fool me.
Joan	Good. I always thought this would be a place for some pickings. The curtains are ever so expensive.
Louie	Oo, my palms itch to get that silver out of that cabinet and into my bag.
Joan	What about the alarm?
Louie	I cut it outside. I'll just snip this wire to be on the safe side.

Joan tampers with the lock

Joan	Some people don't think much of their valuables. Fancy a cheap lock like that.
Louie	It's your skill, darling.

The doorbell rings

Damn!

Joan	Come on, let's scram.
Louie	No, I'm not giving up that easy. They'll go away. Keep quiet.

	The doorbell rings again
Joan	They won't
Louie	I'll have a look out of the side window.
	He goes and then returns
	It's the gasmen. Curse, what do they want?
Joan	Let's go.
	Suddenly two gasmen enter
Gasman 1	Good evening, sir. We've had a report of leaking gas. The front door was not locked so we came in, in case it was serious.
Louie	There's no leaking gas here. I haven't reported it. Have you, dear?
Joan	No, dear. You must have the wrong house. I'll show you out.
Gasman 1	OK, let's quit the fooling. This is not a piece of gas pipe. Hands up. Tie 'em up, Jim.
Louie	What an outrage entering honest citizens' houses and . . .
Gasman 2	Cut the gab. Hands behind your back. I'll just tie up their hands and put this sticking plaster on their gobs.
Joan	Really.
Gasman 1	There's a cupboard under the stairs. They can go in there.
Gasman 2	Come on, you two. Look lively.
	They go out with them and return without them
Gasman 1	Right, I think we'll start on this cabinet of silver. Fancy leaving it open. Some people are careless.
Gasman 2	This is worth a bob or two.
	They are so intent on emptying the cabinet that they do not see a policeman and policewoman creep up behind them
Policeman 1	Right, Muriel.

Police-woman 1	Got him in my best judo grip.
Policeman 1	I'll pick up this gun. You really should look after your weapons, but you were so keen on the loot.
Gasman 2	Would you believe it, the fuzz?
Policeman 1	I arrest you for breaking and entering. I warn you that anything you say will be taken down and used in evidence against you.
Gasman 2	All right, it's a fair cop.
Policeman 1	Fancy screwing a joint disguised as gasmen. I thought that went out years ago.
Police-woman 1	They've brought plenty of Elastoplast.
Policeman 1	Then tie them up with it, Muriel.
Police-woman 1	Right.

She ties up the gasmen

Policeman 1	Put them in the kitchen. We'll tie 'em to the gas cooker – that would be appropriate, I think.

They go out with the gasmen and return without them

You know you can't beat robbing a house disguised as the fuzz. Look, they've put half the stuff in that bag already. I bet their van outside is full of loot. We'll drive away in it.

Police-woman 1	Oo, what lovely silver!

Mr Dewar suddenly enters

Mr Dewar	What are you doing in my house?
Policeman 1	Are you the owner of this property, sir?
Mr Dewar	I am.
Police-woman 1	We had reason to believe your house was being robbed. So we entered and have made an arrest. There are two villains, er, persons disguised as gasmen tied up in your kitchen.

Mr Dewar	Er, how brave of you. Er, thank you.
	Mrs Dewar comes down
Mrs Dewar	That tablet knocked me out. I heard a noise so I came down. I'm so glad you're back, dear. Oh, the police!
Mr Dewar	I'm afraid we were being robbed, dear. This gentleman and lady have caught two thieves.
Mrs Dewar	I feel quite faint.
Police-woman 1	Just sit in this chair, madam.
Mr Dewar	What is the world coming to when a man can't go out for a quiet drink without being robbed.
Policeman 1	And you sit down in this one, sir, it must have been quite a shock.
Mr Dewar	I will. It has been.
Policeman 1	OK, you two are covered. Tie 'em to the chairs, Muriel.
Mr Dewar	What do you mean?
Police-woman 1	We ain't the real fuzz, mate.
Mr Dewar	This is an outrage. You'll never get away with this.
Policeman 1	But we are getting away with it.
	Suddenly the real police break in
Policeman 2	OK you're covered. Drop that gun.
Police-woman 1	The fuzz.
Mrs Dewar	Oh no.
Policeman 2	Untie them.
Policeman 3	Good job we followed them. The Phoney Fuzz Gang. Come on, get them loose.
Police-woman 2	Right, sergeant.
Police-woman 3	I'll soon have you loose, madam.

Mr Dewar	Thank goodness you came. They were going to rob me.
Mrs Dewar	I still feel quite faint.
Police-woman 3	I'll get you a drink
Policeman 3	Search the house to see if there are any more about.
Policeman 2	Right, sergeant.
Mr Dewar	They were taking my silver.
Policeman 3	Oh, they'd clean you out all right.
Police-woman 3	Here's a drink for you, dear.
Mrs Dewar	Thank you.
Police-woman 2	And one for you as well, sir.
Mr Dewar	I certainly need it. It has been a big shock.
Policeman 2	You'll never believe this. Lightfingered Louie and Joan-the-Snatch are tied up under the stairs and Ted and Pete the Gasmen are tied up in the kitchen.
Policeman 3	What a haul. Come on Phoney Fuzz you've got a lot of explaining to do. We'll take a statement from you later, sir. We'll get this lot down to the station.

All the police and crooks go

Mrs Dewar	Quick give me another stiff one.
Mr Dewar	We've got away with it. Let's celebrate.
Mrs Dewar	I don't know how you kept a straight face.
Mr Dewar	And that fainting stuff was pretty convincing.
Mrs Dewar	What a night!
Mr Dewar	It's class that does it. I'm no ordinary tea leaf.

Policeman 2 re-enters

Policeman 2	Just a minute, sir.
Mr Dewar	Yes.

Policeman 2 Could I use your phone? Our radio's on the blink and we need reinforcements for that lot.

Mr Dewar Certainly, officer. Could I thank you for protecting my property?

Policeman 2 All in a day's work, sir. *(on the phone)* Mick, send a wagon and four blokes down to 38 The Boulevard. We've got six villians here. *(to Mr Dewar)* Thank you, sir.

Mr Dewar Goodnight.

Policeman 2 Goodnight. Now what is the correct time?

Mr Dewar Eleven thirty-five, officer. That clock's never wrong.

Policeman 2 That is your clock, sir, in the cabinet.

Mr Dewar Oh no, not that clock, I've never seen that before in my life.

Policeman 2 Then what clock were you referring to, sir?

Mr Dewar I was mixing up that clock and my watch. I'm all confused with this business. I don't know whether I'm coming or going.

Policeman 2 You see that clock fits a description we have.

Mr Dewar Those thieves must have left it.

Policeman 2 You seem to be leaving mud on the carpet, sir.

Mr Dewar I've been doing a bit of gardening.

Policeman 2 In the dark?

Mr Dewar I get so little time in the day.

Policeman 2 If I could just see the soles of your shoes.

Mr Dewar What on earth for?

Policeman 2 Thank you, sir. Just lift up. Oh. I arrest you on suspicion of burglary. We've been looking for that footprint for some time. I must warn you that . . .

Mr Dewar OK, it's a fair cop.

4 Nigel's Foot

Do your family not listen to what each other says? The Tompkins family are like that and they are only interested in their individual lives. See what happens when Nigel Tompkins hurts his foot.

Characters	Nigel Tompkins
	Mrs Tompkins
	Boy
	Gran Tompkins
	Mr Tompkins
	Anne-Marie Tompkins
	Mrs Jenkins
	Rentman

1 The Tompkins' kitchen

Nigel	Mum, I've hurt me foot.
Mrs Tompkins	Don't bother me now, Nigel. Go out and play.
Nigel	But I've hurt me foot.
Mrs Tompkins	Give it a rub. I'm getting the breakfast. Don't you think that's a lovely bit of bacon
Nigel	But I can't stand it.
Mrs Tompkins	But you know you love bacon, Nigel.
Nigel	No, me foot, It hurts.
Mrs Tompkins	Don't get in my way, Nigel. Gran'll be down in a minute and I haven't got her Complan ready.
Nigel	But what shall I do? I can't stand on it.
Mrs Tompkins	Go and sit down for a minute.

A knock at the back door

Go and answer the door, Nigel. I can't leave this bacon.

Nigel	But me foot. You said sit down.
Mrs Tompkins	Never mind your foot. I'm rushed off my feet all day. Go and answer the door.

Nigel hobbles to the back door

Boy	Are you coming back out?
Nigel	I've hurt me foot.
Boy	You shouldn't have played paratroopers.
Nigel	It was your idea to jump off that wall.
Boy	It was Phil's idea. Are you coming out?
Nigel	But me foot.
Mrs Tompkins	Go out and play, Nigel. I don't want you under my feet all day.
Nigel	I'm going to sit down in the lounge.

He shuts the door

Mrs Tompkins	You won't have any friends, if you don't play with them.
Nigel	It's swelling up.
Mrs Tompkins	Let me see. It's only a little bit. Really you do make a fuss. There now the bacon's burnt. You really are the limit, Nigel.

2   *The lounge*

Ten minutes later

Nigel	My foot's getting bigger.
Mrs Tompkins	Well, tell your father.

(Gran enters)

Gran	Have you seen my knitting?
Nigel	I've hurt me foot, Gran.
Gran	You haven't hidden it, have you?
Nigel	It's swelling up.
Mrs Tompkins	Go and sit down, Nigel. I'll get your father. *(calling)* Bert, are you getting up? The bacon's done.
Mr Tompkins	*(from upstairs)* I can smell it burning. I'll be down in a minute.
Mrs Tompkins	Nigel's hurt his foot.
Mr Tompkins	Tell him to rub it.
Mrs Tompkins	Your Dad says rub it.
Nigel	I have rubbed it.
Mrs Tompkins	He says he has rubbed it.

Silence

	Have you gone to sleep again?
Mr Tompkins	No, I haven't. I can't rush with my back.
Nigel	Look it's twice as big as it should be. I've had to take my shoe off.
Mrs Tompkins	You had better take your sock off as well. I don't want that all stretched. That's a new pair.
Gran	I had it in my green bag.
Nigel	Gran, have you got your tape measure? I want to measure my foot.
Gran	It's in my knitting bag. Are you sure you haven't hidden it?
Nigel	No, Gran. Look it's getting too big to stand on. I lean over.

Mrs Tompkins	Then go and sit down, Nigel. Don't bother your Gran.
Nigel	But look, it's three times as big as it should be.
Mrs Tompkins	Yes, it is a bit big. A sprain I think. Or is it a strain? I can never remember. *(calling)* Bert! Nigel's foot is ever so big.
Mr Tompkins	*(from upstairs)* Tell him to rub some cream on it.
Mrs Tompkins	Your Dad says to rub some cream on it.
Nigel	But it's too big to get out of the door. You get it, Mum.
Mrs Tompkins	Really, Nigel, my feet'll wear out waiting on this family.

She goes out as Anne-Marie comes in

Anne-Marie	Did Ted phone?
Mrs Tompkins	Nigel's hurt his foot.
Anne-Marie	He said he would, about tonight.
Nigel	Look at my foot.
Anne-Marie	I hope I haven't upset him.
Nigel	It's four times as big as it should be.
Anne-Marie	I wonder if I should phone him?

Mrs Tompkins comes back in

Mrs Tompkins	Here, rub that in. It's good for cuts, burns, scalds, bruises, stings.

The front door bell rings

Go and answer the door, Anne-Marie.

Anne-Marie	Can't Nigel go?
Nigel	I can't get out of the door.
Anne-Marie	You go, Mum.

Mrs Tompkins	Really I shall be run off my feet today. Bert, are you getting up?
Mr Tompkins	*(from upstairs)* Of course I'm getting up, I'm doing my best.
Mrs Tompkins	Are you going to answer that door, Anne-Marie?
Anne-Marie	I haven't done my hair yet. Why can't Nigel go?
Mrs Tompkins	I have to do everything in this house.

She goes and comes back with Mrs Jenkins

Mrs Jenkins	If I could just have a cup of sugar.
Mrs Tompkins	Yes, Mrs Jenkins. Anne-Marie, get Mrs Jenkins a cup of sugar. Where is that girl?
Anne-Marie	*(from the hall)* I'm doing me hair. Can't Nigel get it?
Gran	*(to Mrs Jenkins)* You haven't seen my knitting, have you?
Mrs Tompkins	That's Mrs Jenkins, Gran, from next door. How can she have seen your knitting? Do put your glasses on.
Gran	I had it in my hands. It must be one of Nigel's tricks.
Mrs Tompkins	I'll get your sugar.

She goes

Nigel	I've hurt me foot.
Mrs Jenkins	How did you do that?
Nigel	I was playing paratroopers. I jumped off the garden wall.
Mrs Jenkins	I told you not to play on my wall.

Mrs Tompkins returns

Mrs Tompkins	Here you are. What do you think of our Nigel's foot?

Mrs Jenkins	I told him not to play on my wall.
Mrs Tompkins	It's getting bigger. Do you think I should get the doctor?
Mrs Jenkins	He doesn't like being called out on Saturdays.
Mrs Tompkins	No.
Mrs Jenkins	No, he plays golf on Saturdays.
Mrs Tompkins	Yes, he plays golf. I forgot that.
Mrs Jenkins	I should rub a bit of butter on it. That's what my mother always did.
Nigel	But it would need a supermarket full of butter.
Mrs Tompkins	Don't be silly, Nigel. Mrs Jenkins is only trying to help.
Mrs Jenkins	Thank you for the sugar.

Mrs Jenkins goes

Nigel	Look, my toe's as big as a shoe.
Mrs Tompkins	I really think you should cut your nails more often, Nigel. Look, you're fetching the wallpaper off.
Nigel	I can't help it. My foot's jammed between the settee and the wall.

Anne-Marie comes back in

Anne-Marie	Has Ted phoned yet? Oh, really, Nigel, you're treading on my newly ironed skirt. Tell him, Mum.
Nigel	I can't help it.
Mrs Tompkins	Now don't you two start quarrelling. Dad, do come and look at our Nigel's foot.
Mr Tompkins	*(from upstairs)* There's no peace in this house is there. I should have thought on my day off I could have a bit of peace. Try wintergreen on it.
Mrs Tompkins	Your Dad says try some wintergreen.

Anne-Marie	We don't want that nasty smelling stuff in this room. What if Ted comes?
Nigel	Can you move the table? My foot's getting wedged under it.
Mrs Tompkins	I can't move the table and get the wintergreen at the same time.
Nigel	But my foot's wedged right under it.
Mrs Tompkins	*(calling)* Bert, you'll have to come down here and shift this table.
Mr Tompkins	You're not starting spring cleaning this morning are you?
Gran	Is it under Nigel?
Mrs Tompkins	Is it under you, Nigel?
Gran	Shift over, Nigel. I want my green knitting bag.
Mrs Tompkins	Do answer your Gran then.
Nigel	Look I can't move a centimetre. I'm stuck.
Gran	You young people are so selfish these days. You don't care about us old folk.

Gran starts to cry

Mrs Tompkins	Now don't start crying, Gran. I'll look in a minute. Do get your glasses on.
Nigel	Can you open a window so I can stick my toes out?
Gran	I don't want to be in a draught. I can't abide draughts. I'll catch my death.

Gran leaves

Mrs Tompkins	Look I can't open windows and get wintergreen. *(calling)* Bert, you must come down here and open a window.
Mr Tompkins	You *are* spring cleaning then.

Mrs Tompkins	No, it's this boy's foot.
Mr Tompkins	One day I'll be glád when he can stand on his own feet and not be a cry baby.
Nigel	I wish I *could* stand on my own feet.

Nigel starts to cry

Mrs Tompkins	Now don't you start as well, Nigel. Bert, you've upset him.
Mr Tompkins	Not so much as he's upset me on my morning off. I'm coming. Oh, my back.
Anne-Marie	Look he's cracked the television tube! Really you are clumsy, Nigel. Ted and I were going to watch this morning.
Nigel	I can't help it. Get the window open.
Mrs Tompkins	Oh I'll do it.
Anne-Marie	Last week he broke my radio.
Mrs Tompkins	Don't you two start quarrelling.

Mr Tompkins enters

Mr Tompkins	Now what's all the fuss about?
Mrs Tompkins	Look at our Nigel's foot.
Mr Tompkins	I've never seen a foot as big as that before. I'll phone.
Mrs Tompkins	For an ambulance?
Mr Tompkins	No, The Guinness Book of Records.
Mrs Tompkins	But don't you think he needs an ambulance?
Mr Tompkins	That foot's too big to get in an ambulance.

Mrs Tompkins	But Bert.
Mr Tompkins	You can't dial 999 for a forklift truck.
Mrs Tompkins	No, I suppose you can't.
Mr Tompkins	Well, I'm off down the pub.
Mrs Tompkins	But you can't go down the pub.
Mr Tompkins	Why not?
Mrs Tompkins	You haven't had your breakfast.

The front door bell rings

Go and answer the door.

Mr Tompkins	I can't have me breakfast and answer the door.
Mrs Tompkins	Oh, I'll go. If only I could put my feet up occasionally.
Nigel	Don't Mum.

Mrs Tompkins comes back in with the Rentman

Rentman	You're not allowed to hang things out of the windows in a council house.
Mrs Tompkins	It's our Nigel's foot.
Rentman	Oh, I say.
Mrs Tompkins	You don't think it's athlete's foot, do you?
Mr Tompkins	He hasn't been running, has he?
Mrs Tompkins	There's some powder for that upstairs.

Rentman	Well I should say . . .
Mrs Tompkins	Yes?
Rentman	That he has put his best foot forward. Ha! Ha!
Mr Tompkins	Or that what he is doing is a great feat. Ha! Ha!
Rentman	Yes, you'll have to . . .
Mrs Tompkins	What?
Rentman	Bring him to heel if he doesn't toe the line. Ha! Ha!
Mr Tompkins	Yes because he's not instep with the rest of us. Ha! Ha!
Rentman	There is one thing though.
Mr Tompkins	What?
Rentman	He certainly has his feet on the ground. Ha! Ha!
Nigel	Don't joke.
Rentman	Sorry. Have I put my foot in it? Ha! Ha!
Mr Tompkins	Yes, you've got off on the wrong foot.
Rentman	And I thought I had not put a foot wrong. I'll just take a photo and then go.
Mrs Tompkins	You can't take a photo with him like that.
Rentman	Why not?
Mrs Tompkins	Well, just look at his hair.

Gran hurries in waving her knitting needles

Gran	I've found my knitting needles.
Mr Tompkins	Watch out what you're doing; you'll have my eye out.
Nigel	Mind my foot, Gran. Ouch!

There is a tremendous explosion. They are all blown out of the room and into the kitchen – except Nigel

Anne-Marie	*(entering)* Was that Ted's bike?
Rentman	My camera!
Mr Tompkins	My back!
Mrs Tompkins	My house!
Gran	My knitting!
Nigel	My foot! Look everyone! My foot's back to normal size. Gran did it with her knitting needles.
Anne-Marie	Nigel, do your hair. I don't want Ted to see you like that.
Mrs Tompkins	We never seem to have a normal Saturday in this house. I do wish we could be like other families.

5 Stagecoach

(A play for idiots only)

There is nothing to say about this play except that you must be crazy to want to read it. If you want to act in it you must first prove to your teacher that you are an idiot.

Characters	Announcer (male or female) Scene-shifter Highwayman Highwaywoman Passenger 1 (female) Boy/Holmes Girl/Watson Woman Mugger Bully Mr Caneum Schoolgirl 1 Schoolgirl 2 Schoolgirl 3 Policeman

1 A stage

Announcer	The scene is a blasted heath in the eighteenth century. Suddenly, by an old gnarled oak . . .
Scene-shifter	Wait a minute, mate, I haven't got the blasted heath in position never mind an oak tree.
Announcer	We can't wait, a highwayman is approaching.
	The sound of a horse
Scene-shifter	Well, blast your heath then, I'm going off for a cup of tea.

Highway-man	Your money or your life.
Highway-woman	The same to you with knobs on.
Highway-man	You can't say that to me. I'm a fearsome highwayman.
Highway-woman	And I'm a fearsome highwaywoman.
Highway-man	You don't have highwaywoman.
Highway-woman	Well, why should men always have the best parts in plays? If you don't let me in to your play, I'll knit you a baggy jumper.
Highway-man	Anything but that! Right, you can be in on this play. I am going to hold up a coach.
Highway-woman	That will be heavy, won't it?
Highway-man	Curses! I'll need a forklift truck.
Highway-woman	They haven't been invented yet.
Highway-man	Nonsense, I've been lifting forks for years.
Highway-woman	I prefer to eat with my fingers.
Highway-man	You don't care who you eat with, do you? Hark a coach approaches.

Sound of horses' hooves

Highway-woman	It sounds like someone banging two coconut shells together.
Highway-man	It is, but don't tell the children. Anyway I like cocoa, you nut.
Highway-woman	I prefer drinking chocolate.

Highway-man	I find the lumps stick in my throat.
Highway-woman	You have to take the silver paper off, you fool!

Sound of horses' hooves

Highway-man	Here it comes. Hands up! Your money or your life.
Passenger 1	But you're only pointing a finger at me.
Highway-man	Ah, but it's a loaded finger.
Passenger 1	Take this jewel.
Highway-man	I can't get it. The carriage is in the way.
Passenger 1	I know. Wait for it . . .

Roll of drums

It's a jewel carriageway!

Highway-man	If all your jokes are as bad as that, I'll saw the ends off two fingers and let you have it.
Passenger 1	That will make them sore.
Highway-man	Put some sticking plaster on her mouth.
Highway-woman	She looks plastered already to me. She is holding ten bottles of brandy.
Highway-man	We must ring them up at once.
Highway-woman	From a tree?
Highway-man	No, I said ring them up not string them up, you fool. The Guinness Book of Records. The world record for holding brandy bottles is only nine.
Passenger 1	I gotta lotta bottle!
Highway-woman	I say, look inside here.

Applause; cries of 'Rhubarb!'

Highway-man Good heavens it's full of actors and actresses.

Passenger 1 That's because. Wait for it . . .

Roll of drums

It's a stage coach!

Highway-woman We could do our play in here.

Highway-man Music please.

Creepy music

Announcer We present 'Mystery of the Moors'!

Boy Can I be in your play?

Girl Can I as well?

Highway-woman If you can squeeze into this coach.

Groans are heard

Passenger 2 Shift over.

Passenger 3 You're on my foot.

Highway-man Right, are we all set?

Boy I play Sherlock Holmes.

Girl And I play Doctor Watson.

Passenger 2 Why is he called Watson?

Passenger 1 He is called Watson . . . wait for it . . .

Roll of drums

. . . because he always knows 'What's on' the telly!

Applause

Announcer The scene is Baker Street.

Sound of tube train

	Not the tube station, you fool, Dr Holmes's residence 221B Baker Street.
Scene-shifter	All right, I'm doing my best. Blasted heath one minute, Baker Street the next . . .
Announcer	A woman staggers up the stairs.
Woman	My God, Holmes, you must help me.
Holmes	Why?
Woman	Because I've no other home to go to.
Passenger 1	I thought I was doing the jokes round here.
Woman	Aaah!
Watson	She's fainted, Holmes.
Holmes	Why has she fainted Watson?
Watson	The blood has not got to her brain.
Holmes	I don't mean the medical reason, you fool. What is the mystery of this young and beautiful woman. She is so beautiful yet . . .
Watson	Yet what Holmes?
Holmes	She has never been on page 3 of *The Sun*.
Watson	There is a note clutched in her hand, Holmes.
Holmes	What does it say?
Watson	I promise to pay the bearer one pound.
Holmes	Give me my magnifying glass, Watson.
Watson	What is it, Holmes?
Holmes	Great Scott, it's a pound note.
Watson	Brilliant deduction, Holmes.
Holmes	Quick put it in the till.
	Sound of old shop till
	Now give me my pipe and violin.
Watson	You're going to play while you work out the mystery, Holmes?

Holmes	No, it's time for the Country and Western festival at Wembley, you fool.
Woman	Ah . . .
Watson	She's coming round, Holmes.
Holmes	Don't be an idiot, she's here already.
Watson	No, I mean out of her faint.
Woman	The moors, the moors, the moors . . .
Holmes	I hope she says that again.
Watson	Why, Holmes?
Holmes	Because all the more the merrier.
Woman	The hound of the . . .
Watson	She's fainted again.
Holmes	Quick we must get to the moors.
Watson	Why?
Holmes	There are more reasons than I can tell you. We must be quick. We'll have to fly by Concorde.
Watson	But it hasn't been invented yet.
Holmes	Curses, we'll have to go by train.

Sound of train followed by sound of owl hooting and ghostly wind

Watson	God, it's creepy here on the moor. Have you ever known anything so creepy, Holmes?
Holmes	Yes, class 1A doing all their homework.
Watson	What's that over there?
Holmes	Where?
Watson	By that rock.
Holmes	God, it's huge, it's hairy, it's got fangs, it's got scales, it's got red burning eyes, and look at those claws.
Watson	Have you ever seen anything like it before?
Holmes	Yes it looks like my Maths teacher.

Watson	It's coming closer.
Holmes	It's time we moved.
Watson	Where to?
Holmes	The next scene of the play.
Watson	Where's that?
Holmes	Strange Hill Comprehensive School.
Scene-shifter	Look I've only just set up the moors scene. Now you want a school. It gets worse.
Announcer	Yes, what could be worse than Strange Hill Comprehensive? In the splendid grounds Mugger and Bully are talking.
Mugger	I say, Bully, there are some nice first years over there. Let's give them some money so they can buy some tuck.
Bully	What a ripping idea. And I'll see if I can help them with their homework.
Mugger	Here comes that nice Mr Caneum. Did you do all your five million sums for homework?
Bully	No, I only managed four million.
Mugger	You'll catch it.
Mr Caneum	Gis a fag, Mugger, or I'll punch your 'ead in.
Mugger	I would never carry cigarettes, sir. They are bad for your health.
Mr Caneum	Get to your classroom, stupid idiots.
Announcer	4C's classroom.
Schoolgirl 1	Let us put an apple on the desk for Mr Caneum.
Schoolgirl 2	Oh, I do hope we have a nice hard lesson again.
Schoolgirl 3	With plenty of homework.
Schoolgirl 1	Quiet, class, here comes Mr Caneum.
Mr Caneum	Right, you lot, stick your hands up.
Schoolgirl 2	But you've not got a gun, sir.

Mr Caneum	This finger is loaded.
Highway-man	We've used that joke.
Mr Caneum	Sorry. I've only just got into this play. Put your knees up instead or I'll throw this table at you.
Schoolgirl 3	Why not throw it twelve times, sir.
Mr Caneum	Why?
Passenger 1	Then . . . wait for it . . .
	Roll of drums
	They'll know their twelve times table.
Mr Caneum	Right, I'm holding you all to ransom. Write out ransom notes to your parents. I want a million pounds or I'll cut your ears off.
Policeman	'Ere . . . 'ere . . . 'ere, you can't do that.
Mr Caneum	How did you get into this play?
Policeman	Isn't this studio seven?
Announcer	No, this is Strange Hill Comprehensive.
Policeman	Sorry, I'm in the wrong play.
Schoolgirl 1	And I thought that nice policeman would rescue us.
Mr Caneum	Ha! Ha! You are in my power.
Schoolgirl 2	That is why . . .
Passenger 1	Wait for it . . .
	Roll of drums
	We are all so shocked!
Schoolgirl 3	There's only one thing we can do.
Schoolgirl 1	What is that?
Schoolgirl 3	Send for the US Cavalry.
Scene-shifter	Oh no, I'm not having any of that. This is ridiculous.

Sound of trumpet

Schoolgirl 2	They're coming. We're saved.
Holmes	Just a minute, I'm supposed to save you.
Highway-man	This gets worse and worse. I wish we had never started it. Shall we ride to York?
Highway-woman	What for?
Highway-man	To get a Yorkie Bar. It must be the interval by now.
Policeman	Irish stew all in the name of the law for telling old jokes. What a haul! There'll be promotion in this for me.

Silly music and groans.

6 The Egg Play

Can you outsmart Sherlock Holmes and Dr. Watson?
Will they find Moriarty? Will the chickens get them first.
What have eggs got to do with all this? Read on ...

Characters	Narrator
	Holmes
	Watson
	Farmer Giles
	Lady
	Housekeeper
	Flower-seller
	Voice

1 *221B Baker Street*

Narrator	The scene is 221B Baker Street, the home of that ace sleuth Sherlock Holmes, on a foggy night. A doorbell rings.
Holmes	The phone. Watson.
Watson	It's the door, Holmes.
Holmes	How do you know it's the door?
Watson	Phones haven't been invented yet.
Holmes	What brilliant deduction, Watson. I can see you are improving. Hand me my magnifying glass.
Watson	What for, Holmes?
Holmes	To find the door, you fool.
Watson	It's by the bookcase.
Holmes	Ah yes. Stand back, Watson. Hand me my gun. This may be a trick.
Watson	A conjuror, Holmes?

Holmes	No, you fool. It could be . . . dare I say it . . . Moriarty.
Watson	What can we do?
Holmes	This needs all my brain power. Hand me my violin.
Watson	You can't play a violin holding a gun.
Holmes	I'll fiddle it somehow.
Watson	Why not just ask who's there?
Holmes	He could be in disguise, you fool. I'll peep through the keyhole. Bah, nothing.
Watson	The key's still in the lock, Holmes.
Holmes	Ah yes. I see a man in a straw hat, a smock, and muddy boots. He has straw sticking out of his hair and he carries a pitchfork.
Watson	What could he be?
Holmes	Can't you tell by the smell?
Watson	No, Holmes.
Holmes	It's the Avon Lady, you fool.
Watson	Let her in. It may put us on the scent of a new mystery.

Farmer Giles enters

Farmer Giles	Mr Holmes, I be Farmer Giles. I do bring thee a great egg-laying mystery to solve.
Holmes	I don't think I could tackle that.
Watson	Don't be chicken about it, Holmes.
Holmes	You're right, Watson. What is the mystery?
Farmer Giles	I shell tell you. My hens be not laying.
Holmes	Can't they sit instead?
Farmer Giles	No, they be laying no eggs. Nor be Farmer Williams's, nor be Farmer Harris's. There no eggs in the whole of Wessex.

Holmes	How eggstrawdinary! Here is a mystery to unscramble. Hand me my violin, Watson.
Watson	You already have it.
Holmes	Just a quick burst of Country and Western. *Violin plays* I have it. It's eggstreamly simple.
Farmer Giles	What?
Watson	What?
Holmes	Someone is poaching them!
Watson	I prefer mine fried.

A lady dashes in – she is very upset

Lady	I've been to the market. Eggs are up again.
Watson	That must be painful for the chickens.
Holmes	Watson!
Watson	It was only a yoke, Holmes.
Holmes	There is no time for jokes, Watson. I eggspect Moriarty is behind this.
Watson	You don't say, Holmes.
Holmes	I did say it, you fool. Quick, to the county of Wessex!
Lady	I have a horse and cart outside.
Watson	I can't see one in the road?
Lady	No, it's in the corridor. I had a job getting it up the stairs.

Holmes' housekeeper enters

House-keeper	I put up with your funny ways, Mr Holmes, but I do draw the line at a horse and cart on the landing.
Holmes	You're paid to housekeep not be an artist. If we do not come back, write to this box number of *The Times*.

2 A street

Outside in the thick fog a flower girl approaches Holmes

Flower-seller	Buy a flower off a poor girl, sir.
Holmes	This is no time for Homes and Gardens commercials.
Flower-seller	I haven't eaten for two days, sir.
Holmes	Oh, all right. Just a minute. Why is this flower getting bigger and bigger?
Flower-seller	It's a self-raising flower, Mr Holmes.
Holmes	Here's a sovereign.
Flower-seller	Let me put it in your buttonhole.
Holmes	Thank you.

3 A country lane

There is a clip clop of horse's hooves (coconuts)

Watson	Don't you think they should have told us that this was a manure cart, Holmes.
Holmes	I knew all the time, Watson. I wanted to put Moriarty off the scent. Strange, here we are buried in this manure and I can smell nothing but this flower. Oh, no!
Watson	What is it?
Holmes	That flower-seller was Moriarty! This flower is strangling me. Urgh! I shall eggspire!
Narrator	Tune in next week to find out what happens. Will Holmes and Watson get out of the mess they are in? What is the eggsplanation of the non-laying hens?

4 *The same*

One week later

Watson	That rest did me good, Holmes.
Holmes	You fool, I've been strangled by this poisonous flower all week. Do something!
Watson	I've no weed-killer, Holmes.
Holmes	Think of something.
Watson	Miss World.
Holmes	What do you mean, Miss World?
Watson	You said think of something.
Holmes	To get me out of this, you fool.
Watson	Just a minute. I'm a doctor. I'll get out my scalpel and give it a prune.
Holmes	Better give me the prune. That will loosen me.
Watson	There you are – free.
Holmes	I'm forty-three, you fool. Now jump out of this cart and hide in this hen house.
Watson	I don't want to be cooped up there.
Holmes	It is the best way to find out about the mystery as sure as eggs is eggs.
Watson	Shouldn't it be as sure as eggs *are* eggs.
Holmes	We've no time to think about grammar. I eggspect Moriarty here at any moment.
Watson	You're putting all your eggs in one basket, Holmes.
Holmes	There are no eggs, you fool. That's what the whole play is about.
Watson	Sorry, Holmes. I'm getting a bit addled by all this.
Holmes	Moriarty is a very hard-boiled criminal. Just think Watson, if we don't solve this mystery . . .
Watson	Moriarty will corner the world egg market?

Holmes	No, Watson. I can hardly say it, there will be . . . there will be . . .
Watson	Yes, Holmes.
Holmes	There will be no more egg and spoon races.
Watson	How eggseedingly bad, Holmes.
Holmes	Quick, Watson, there's someone coming.
Voice	Who be in there?
Holmes	Sssh!
Voice	Who be in there, I say?
Holmes	There ain't nobody here but us chickens.
Voice	That's all right then.
Watson	Brilliant, Holmes.
Narrator	And so Holmes and Watson sat up with the chickens. It was a fowl night.
Holmes	Keep your pecker up, Watson. Here, read this play 'Omelette' by William Shakespeare.
Watson	Don't you mean 'Hamlet', Holmes?
Holmes	That's a cigar, you fool.
Watson	Someone is coming, Holmes.
Holmes	Let me look out. He has a bag. He is going to feed the chickens.
Watson	Is it?
Holmes	It could be. Ah, as I suspected, Watson. He's feeding the chickens invisible corn. The chickens have been laying all the time but they are laying invisible eggs.
Watson	How corny can you get?
Holmes	But I have the antidote. I'll just inject this chicken with this.
	Clucking sounds
Watson	It's laying an egg. Brilliant, Holmes. A blue egg, a red egg, a golden egg. There is writing on them.

Holmes	Read what is says, Watson.
Watson	Cadbury's Creme Eggs. We're rich, Holmes.
Holmes	Don't be a fool, Watson. You can't crack silver paper.
Watson	So Holmes?
Holmes	So, Watson, Moriarty has triumphed again. What an eggseptional criminal he is.

Activities
What's funny about that?

Crazy Court

Ush! Ush! Ush!
Why are you saying 'Ush!'?
I'm the Usher.

How do you plead?
Quite badly, if I cut myself shaving.
Plead! Not bleed, you fool.

I have my briefs here, mi lud.
I should hope so. I want no one in my court without underpants.

Nigel's Foot

Well I should say that he has put his best foot forward...
Or that what he is doing is a great feat.
Yes, you'll have to bring him to heel if he doesn't toe the line.

★ Make a list of all the 'silly jokes' you can find in the plays.

★ Tell each other any other silly jokes like these that you know. Practise them in pairs. Then present them to the rest of the class.

Stagecoach

The Egg Play

The moors, the moors, the moors . . .
I hope she says that again.
Why, Holmes?
Because all the more the merrier.

How many egg words, like *eggstreamly* can you find in *The Egg Play?*

How eggstraordinary! Here is a mystery to unscramble. I have it. It's eggstreamly simple.

I've been to the market. Eggs are up again.
That must be painful for the chickens.
Watson!
It was only a yoke, Holmes.

★ Make a Joke Book. Start off by writing in the ones above.
Can you find any cracker jokes?
funny graffiti?
knock knock jokes?
elephant jokes?

★ Choose your favourite jokes and draw some cartoons to go with them.

Act out!

Use a cassette-recorder

1 Act out a scene in which the Tufton family meet up with the person who recommended their holiday cottage.

2 You and your family have rented a holiday home. You arrive to find that another family are already there. Act out the scene.

3 At the end of *It's a Fair Cop* imagine that the real police in fact turn out to be *more* of the Phoney Fuzz gang. Act out what happens next.

4 The Tompkins family are not interested in Nigel's problem. Imagine something serious has happened to *you* but no one in your family cares. You sit down at the breakfast table with them, determined to make them take notice. Act out the scene.

5 You have had a series of burglaries at your house. Dr Watson and Sherlock Holmes arrive to investigate. Act out the scenes which follow. Make them as funny as you can.

★ When you have acted out one of the scenes, write out a script.

> Make your play lively and fun to act.
> When you have worked at it, write out the script neatly.
> Try it out. Tape it. Play it to the group.
> Make a programme and a poster for your play.
> Give it a good title.

Write on

1 You have been arrested and brought to court. You enter the courtroom to see some very unusual things: the judge in jeans, lawyers drinking beer, the police playing cards. Write an amusing story about what happened to you on trial.

2 Make a list of all the things which were wrong with the Tuftons' holiday cottage.

3 Write an advert for the holiday cottage which makes it sound wonderful and ideal.

4 Write your own short story called *It's a Fair Cop.*

5 'We never seem to have a normal Saturday in this house.' Write a short story which begins or ends with these words.

Be a designer

1 Choose any three characters from the plays. Draw/paint their portraits. Compare your pictures with others in your group.

2 Design a poster to advertise any of these plays.

3 Draw a scene from *one* of the plays. It could be the Crazy Court, the Holiday Cottage or even Nigel's Foot!

Write a silly play
Make plans

★ What is your play going to be about? Think of a subject that interests you and will interest an audience. Why will it be silly?

★ How many people are going to be in the play?

★ Think of some amusing names for your characters. You could use a telephone directory! Are they going to be:
  male or female?
  young or old?
  humans or animals?
  English or Chinese or Dutch?
  (they will need to *speak* English!)

★ Where will the action take place?
  a classroom   in a hole
  a beach   around the dinner-table
  your garden   a courtroom

★ How many different scenes will there be? Or will the action be in one place only?

★ What time of the day, week, or year is your play set?

★ If you aim to perform your play to an audience you will need:
  sets   costumes
  lighting   music
  props   sound effects